EVOLUTION,
FACT OR THEORY?

By Cora A. Reno

MOODY PRESS

CHICAGO

Printed in the United States of America

CONTENTS

INTRODUCTION

BY PAUL HUTCHENS

As FAR as I am concerned, the theory of evolution has long been a dead issue, dead as the fragments of bones from which Pithecanthropus erectus was reconstructed.

However, to many people, it is very much alive; and, as the author of this book points out, it is being taught as a fact in many high schools, colleges and universities. Thousands of our young people arc unaware that there is sufficient evidence to convince many scientists that evolution's claims are not well grounded.

With calm logic, Miss Reno defends the view of the creationists because it has greater weight of evidence to support it than has the theory of evolution. In my judgment she has successfully refuted the chief arguments of the proponents of the evolutionary theory.

Reading her skillfully written book could be likened to watching a post-mortem, while the author as an experienced medical examiner performs the autopsy. Not only do we find no signs of actual life, but the cause of death—starvation for lack of evidence—is apparent.

By way of personal testimony, I should like to say that to make evolution a part of my "knowledge," I would have to discard from my thinking many things that are absolute: primarily, I would have to divorce my heart from the Christ of the Bible, who is revealed therein as the very Son of God. He is the Supreme Fact. He is absolutely *absolute*. That is, according to the definition of the term, He is not dependent or relative, but is determined in Himself, and not by anything outside Himself.

Some time ago I ran across a carefully written brochure on *The Other Side of Evolution*, authored by Luke Woodard, a brilliant Quaker. In it, he says: "Evolution's theory of Christ's advent presents Him as 'the culmination of the process in the realm of personality, the crown of divine effort working at the heart of humanity through all the ages that preceded His coming.' Hence, according to the theory, He pre-existed only in the successive

stages from lower to higher until the process cul-
minated in divinity."

The writer then goes on to say, "Evolution's
Christ had a beginning. Our adorable Christ says,
'I am the Alpha and Omega, the beginning and the
ending. I am the first and the last.' The inspired
record (in the Gospel of St. John) says: 'In the
beginning existed the Word; and the Word was
face to face with God; yea, the Word was God
Himself. He is the One who was face to face with
God in the beginning" (1:1, 2).

"He was made flesh by being miraculously con-
ceived and born of the Virgin Mary. This was no
one-hundred-thousand-year process."

Instead of progressing through the ages to something higher, to Divinity itself, He being Deity from
the beginning came from Heaven to earth and dwelt
among us—*God manifest in the flesh*.

Evolution, if I accepted it, would rob me of the
Lord Jesus Christ because it would make Him the
result of an evolutionary process rather than the
Creator of all things and the One who existed before all things. It would rob Him of His deity,
make Him a liar, and strip Him of His power to
forgive sin.

I have another deep personal interest in this

book: among the thousands who are now finding
their classrooms a place of mental confusion, are
many who a few years ago were happy-go-lucky
boys and girls reading my Sugar Creek Gang
books; they were being influenced by them to clean
living and faith in God, taking the Lord Jesus Christ
at His Word, and giving their hearts to Him in
love and dedication to do His will. Now many
of these are in high school and college and are
having to choose between believing in the God
of Creation and yielding to the claims of "the antagonistic theory of evolution" with all its tragic
consequences.

I say *tragic*, because as our Lord Himself has
taught, "As a man thinketh in his heart, so is he."
Both a man's character and his conduct are determined by his thoughts. Hence my strong recom-
mendation of this book of common sense, written
by a consecrated young science teacher who not
only loves the Bible and its Christ, but really
knows evolution's claims.

This book will be read also by many science
students who may not be particularly concerned
with the moral issues involved. They are interested
primarily in examining the evidence against evolution. Perhaps you are one of these. Up to the

present you may not have known that there is such a vast amount of evidence against evolution. I suggest that you give Miss Reno's work unbiased study to see if she has not been absolutely fair to evolution's claims, while at the same time she demonstrates that the creationist's view is the more logical of the two.

This book should produce a crisis in your thinking and in your life. It will show you the secret of true happiness, for which, if you are a normal person, you are earnestly searching.

In the New Testament quotations, Miss Reno has used the Williams' Translation.

Chapter 1

THIS PROBLEM OF EVOLUTION

MAYBE YOU ARE ONE of the many students whose science classroom has become a bewildering place. Perhaps you too have been confused by the subject of evolution.

If you are a Christian, you are in an especially difficult position. In a godly home, and in church and Sunday school, you were taught the facts of creation as presented in the Bible. In your classroom you are in an entirely foreign atmosphere, faced with the theory of evolution. You don't know which to believe—the Biblical account or the evolutionary theory.

You consider your teachers educated men and women whose word is to be accepted as true; yet what they teach and apparently believe very often contradicts the Word of God. The authors of your textbooks, presumably, are authorities in their fields; yet their teaching is based on the theory of evolution.

This book is designed to lead you out of the labyrinth in which you have been wandering—for the Bible and true science cannot be in conflict. The one is the *Word* of God, the other the *works* of God, and they are always in perfect agreement.

Because many who read this book may be unfamiliar with the language of the classroom, and may have little background in science, the use of technical expressions has been avoided. This book is intended especially for you who are in high school, but it will also be useful to all who are interested in young people.

If you are puzzled by the problem of evolution, we hope that you will come to see that it is a mere theory which is unsustained by scientific proof and that the facts of science do give support to the doctrine of creation. Our desire is that if you already believe the Bible to be the Word of God, your faith will be greatly strengthened. Then, with your feet firmly planted on the only true and solid foundation, you will be encouraged to take your stand for what you know to be right. This will require courage, for it is usually easier to drift with the current than it is to oppose wrong.

However, courage alone is not enough. Yo also need accurate information. This book is designed to help give you that information.

Now a word of counsel about standing for what is right. More often than not, harm is done by arguing in the classroom; cool discussion with individuals in small groups produces better and more lasting results. If the matter is brought up in class and you find yourself in rather warm disagreement with your textbook, or with your instructor, or with a fellow student, remember the old adage, "It is better to *use* your temper than to *lose* it." You should be prepared by prayer for such a situation, so that you will know what to say and how to say it in a truly Christlike manner, not unnecessarily antagonizing anyone. Often, a well-chosen remark or question is helpful in stimulating the thinking of the group. Strive earnestly to maintain a kindly spirit and a nonargumentative manner.

In the back of this book you will find a chart giving a partial analysis of the evolutionary teaching in some of the most commonly used high school biology texts in our country. By using this chart you may see which books being used in your own classes are still teaching all or some of the time-worn arguments of the evolutionary theory.

You may be surprised to note how universally this theory is being taught, not as a theory only, but as a fact. A theory is valuable *if* it causes people to examine *both* sides of a question; but the danger of the present situation is found in the way evolution is being presented—not as the unproved theory that it is, but rather as a scientifically established fact.

In *Biology for You*, we find this statement: "All reputable biologists have agreed that evolution of life on the earth is an established fact."[1] In *Everyday Biology* we read, "There is much evidence besides that found in a study of fossils to show that present living things descended from those of earlier times. . . . The evidence secured from various scientific fields has made it possible for scientists to find the relationships of organisms now living not only to one another, but also to those which once lived but long since have become extinct."[2] *Exploring Biology* states, "No one has discovered a single fact to disprove the theory of evolution, and the facts that establish its truth are abundant."[3]

---

[1] B. B. Vance, and D. F. Miller, *Biology for You* (J. B. Lippincott Company, 1950), p. 580.

[2] F. C. Curtis, and O. W. Caldwell, and Sherman, *Everyday Biology* (Ginn & Company, 1946), p. 621.

[3] Ella Thea Smith, *Exploring Biology* (Harcourt, Brace & Company, 1949), p. 488.

Throughout America there are many Christian teachers of science who present to their classes *both* sides of this question. In spite of the fact that we would like to be optimistic about the situation, we are compelled to admit that the majority of our young people hear only one side, that of the evolutionist.

This book will give you the "other side" of evolution. The most commonly found arguments in favor of evolution are considered briefly in the order in which they are given in the chart. Following the presentation of each argument there is a short discussion of some of the reasons why it is not valid.

Before presenting these arguments for evolution and our factual refutations, let's clarify the meaning of the word *evolution*. As we use the term we do not simply mean *change*, but evolution in the sense the biologist understands it.

"The theory that new types arise from preceding types, the more complex forms appearing as the descendants of the simpler ones, so that all living things bear a relationship to one another, is called the theory of *organic evolution*."[4]

---

[4] E. Kroeber and W. H. Wolff, *Adventures with Animals and Plants*, (D. C. Heath & Co., 1948), p. 553.

"The theory of evolution is a complex idea. It states that all living things are related to one another because they all came from the same common ancestor far back in geological times. It states that new species arose from preceding species of plants and animals that were simpler, that this has been happening since plants and animals first existed on this earth, and that it is still going on. This statement of the theory of organic evolution is commonly accepted by biologists."[5]

Two questions immediately arise: 1) Is this theory scientifically sound? 2) Is it taught in the Bible? Can a person who accepts the Bible as the inspired Word of the Creator believe in the theory of organic evolution?

In Genesis we are told that God created things "after their kind." The word *kind* as used here might have a variety of meanings. There surely is room for a wide variety of interpretations. However, there is not room to include all of the ideas that accompany the theory of evolution.

It seems reasonable to assume that *kind* as used in such places as Genesis 1:21, 24, 25 refers to types which can interbreed. We can be quite sure that there were not as many kinds of groups then as

[5] Kroeber and Wolff, p. 561.

there are *species* in our present system of classification. It is a matter of common observation that the offspring of any plant or animal can be very different from the parent. Within our own lifetime we have seen developed new species of such flowers as daisies and gladioli, and new kinds of cattle and dogs.

The evolutionist says that all of the living forms found today have been produced from one common ancestor. We agree that in the past there has been *change*, but there is not convincing evidence to support the theory that there has been this much change. As we proceed we will call attention to the amount of change that can be produced by artificial and natural means. In a certain sense this change might be called "evolution," but we will not so use the word. As we use it here, we mean change from one group to another so that all of the living things in the world, including man, are related one to the other.

We hope that you will do some critical thinking as you read; many have accepted the theory of evolution without doing any real thinking for themselves. They may have accepted it because they found it so widely taught; or, they may have been influenced to believe it because it was so ingeniously presented; or, perhaps because some very learned people sincerely believe it. These criteria are not satsifactory means of judging the validity of the theory of evolution.

Chapter 2

ARGUMENT—SIMILARITY PROVES RELATIONSHIP

EIGHT OF THE eleven textbooks analyzed present the idea that similarity of structure proves relationship. This idea is based largely on comparative anatomy. A scientist will study, for instance, the skeleton of a fish, a frog, a snake, a bird, and a cat. Noting the similarities, he will then study the muscular, digestive, circulatory, and nervous systems in the same way. If he is an evolutionist, he will likely conclude that the nearer alike these animals are as to structure, the more nearly related they are in evolutionary descent. In fact, he is likely to say that this is the only logical way to account for the similarities. The illustration is often used that the flipper of a whale, the wing of a bird, the foreleg of a horse, and the arm of man are formed according to a common plan. *Biology and Human Affairs* sums up what most of the books teach: "The resemblances among living things are explained by the theory that they are all akin, that the different forms of life on the earth have developed from one first simple kind and all trace back to the same ancestry. If this belief is correct, it is not surprising that all living things are alike in their basic structure and their fundamental life processes; that man in his physical being has something in common with the grass of the field and the strange creatures of the ocean's depths."[1]

REFUTATION

There are several weaknesses in this argument. One is found in the interpretation of the facts. That there are similarities among living things, all will agree. However, the resemblances do not *prove* evolution, for the facts can equally well be said to show special creation. What then can be the cause of these similarities? First of all, they could be the result of a common plan in the mind of God. There is no reason why He should not have used a similar general plan for many plants and animals. It is logical to think that He might use the same plan for animals that were to walk the same earth, breathe the same air and eat the same food. The

---

[1] Ritchie, John W., *Biology and Human Affairs* (World Book Co., 1948), p. 38.

Great Designer might have used another general plan for animals which were to fly in the air, and another for those which were to live in the sea.

God is omnipotent. We believe that He could have used a different plan for each animal; He could have created all kinds of weird animals with different combinations of numbers of legs, ears, eyes and heads. It is not a question of what He is able to do, but what He actually did. As creationists, we believe that God created groups of plants and animals according to a general plan and gave them certain similarities at the time they were made.

A second reason for similarity of structure among certain groups of plants or animals is that they really have descended from a common ancestor! This may sound as though we are admitting evolution, but we are not. We admit that there has been and can be *change within a group*. All of those who believe the Biblical account concerning man agree that the various races of men on the earth today descended from Adam and Eve. From them as the ancient ancestors we have a great variety of men from the short, dark Pygmies to the tall, blond Nordics. The difference found among men today, however, is merely change

within a group. It is no harder to believe that all
of our breeds of dogs came from an original pair
of dogs, and likewise our many breeds of horses
from an original pair of horses, than to believe
these facts about the changes that have taken place
between Adam and modern men. *Christian* teachers of science do not all agree as to *how much*
similarity may be due to common ancestry, but
they do agree that this is the cause of some of these
similarities.

In Genesis we are told that God created living
things after their kind. Exactly what this means
we may never know until we get to Heaven! In the
world today there are a million and more different
species of plants and animals. In our commonly
used system of classification, we divide plants and
animals into large groups called phyla. Phyla
are subdivided into classes; classes into orders;
orders into families; families into genera; and
genera into species. We can be quite certain that
the group called a "species" is not what is referred
to in Genesis by the word "kind." We are not sure
which of these groups in our classification were
special creations and which have descended from
others. In some cases the first member of a *family*
may have been specially created, and in others it

may have been a genus or species. There is reason
to think that at least the phyla, classes, and orders
were specially created. Changes and modifications
from these special creations give us the great variety of forms we find today. We think it is improba-
ble that Noah's ark (450' x 75' x 45', Gen. 6) con-
tained all of our present species. Very likely it did
not contain all such dogs as poodles, collies, shep-
herds, bulldogs and terriers. Many of these have developed in recent years from other breeds by such
methods as selection, mutation or crossing to get
hybrids. The fact that plants and animals are being developed today in no way proves the theory
that all came from a common ancestor. This change
and development can take place only *within* certain specially created groups such as the phyla,
classes and orders.

Another difficulty in trying to prove evolution
by structural similarities is that it cannot be carried
out consistently. Certain parts of some animals
show great likeness to the same parts of other animals, whereas different parts of these animals show
dissimilarities. One example is that of the Tasmanian wolf and the dog. The likeness of their skeletons is used by the evolutionist as a proof of their
close relationship. However, the Tasmanian wolf

is a marsupial, carrying its young in a pouch, but the dog is not. This latter fact proves that the two are not closely related.

Another example is found in the African scorpion and the lobster, each of which has a large pinching claw. According to the evolutionist, this resemblance should show close relationship, and yet in this case he says that they are distantly related because the claws are on different appendages. These are not just isolated examples, for we find many such cases in which similarity does not prove relationship. Sometimes internal structures will show one thing and external structures another. It is hard for a person to be consistent when he argues that similarity proves relationship.

Chapter 3

ARGUMENT—PROOF OFFERED FROM GEOLOGY

You will see by the chart* that more space is devoted to the study of geology and paleontology than to any other one subject. It is stated that the deeper one goes into the layers of rocks, the simpler are the fossils found. It is said that these simple plants and animals developed first and that all present forms have evolved from them. The argument presented from this field is well summed up in one of our books:

"Fossils are remains—imprints, traces, petrified or actual forms—of ancient plants or animals preserved through the ages in rocks, tar pits, or frozen tundra. While strata of rocks are often upturned, twisted, and contorted from their original layered appearance, scientists have been able to arrange them in the order in which they were deposited and thus to form the geologic timetable, which re-

*See pp 126, 127

27

veals the order of development, of evolution, of plants and animals.

"When all fossils are placed in the correct time-table as revealed by the rocks in which they were trapped, a succession of organisms developing from simple to more and more complex is disclosed. The oldest rocks show no fossils; the first ones to show living things disclose signs of the simplest plants and animals, namely the bacteria and Protozoa. Appearing in later rocks, in the order named, were signs of simple one-celled green plants and invertebrates, and then more complex invertebrates and vertebrates—fishes, amphibians, reptiles, birds and mammals, including man. The plant life of the rock record also developed in an ascending order of complexity."[1]

REFUTATION

The subject which concerns fossils in general is one of the most interesting in all of the field relating to biology and evolution. Here we have actual proof of what living things were like in the past. Fossils are plants or animals or their parts or imprints, preserved in ice, tar, amber, rock, or other substances. These all have a story to tell us. It is

---

[1]F. M. Wheat and E. T. Fitzpatrick, *Biology* (American Book Co., 1949), p. 420.

a story which we should study carefully if we hope
to learn more about the way God has worked in our
world in the past. Sad to say, some guesswork and
speculation have entered into the interpretation of
this story as can be seen in the quotation just given.
The guesswork, involving such things as recon-
structing a whole skeleton from just a small fragment of bone, is often confused with the parts of
the story which are factual. However, for the most
part, the material concerning fossils as found in
biology texts is fairly reliable. The actual facts
about fossils as found by leading scientists throughout the years only serve to confirm the Genesis
record. Therefore, do not be afraid to study this
record thoroughly.

Some of the facts as given here may be new to
you. We ask you to consider them carefully. As
Christians, we should always be ready to accept
the truth. Some sincere people have allowed themselves to become so opinionated that their minds
are often closed to new discoveries, especially in
this field. Their unwillingness to accept new ideas,
which can be substantiated beyond the shadow of
a doubt, often makes them the laughing-stock of
those who have made a thorough study of fossils.
This in itself would not be so serious if it did not

bring the cause of Christ into disrepute and serve to alienate those we would like to see won to Him. Consider the facts given in the next few paragraphs and think them over carefully; do not discard them just because they are different from what you have learned in the past.

Many people believe that if we admit the earth is very old we are conceding ground to the evolutionist. This is not true. There is nothing inconsistent with our belief in the verbal inspiration of the Genesis account and our agreement with the geologists that our earth is millions of years old. In many of your Bibles you will find the date 4004 B.C. beside Genesis 1:1. This date, supplied by a man named Ussher who lived in the seventeenth century, is of course not part of the inspired record. So much has been learned about the Bible and science since Ussher lived that few thinking Christians today can accept all the dates he has suggested.

The proofs that our earth is very old are irrefutable. If we face facts, we have to agree with the geologists who estimate its age to be something over two billion years. If you are interested in the various ways of arriving at these figures, there are many books on the subject which you may read. I mention some of these ways without attempting to analyze their values and weaknesses. We need to be careful not to confuse the proofs of the earth's great age with the interpretation sometimes given by the evolutionists.

"One such method (of estimating the age of the earth) is based on calculation of the rate of sedimentation and rock formation. A second method involves the calculation of the rate of erosion of land areas. The rate at which the oceans are increasing in salt concentration is the basis for a third method of determining geological age."[2]

"Physicists estimate the age of any rock containing uranium (or some other radioactive substance) in another way. It has been shown that uranium disintegrates slowly, forming an isotope of lead. Knowing how long it takes to form one gram of lead in this way, physicists measure the amount of uranium-derived lead in rocks of this type. Then they estimate how long it would take for this amount of lead to be produced by the disintegration of uranium. By this method rocks from one past period have been shown to be some five hundred million years old. The oldest known sample of

[2] G. W. Hunter and F. K. Hunter, *Biology in Our Lives* (American Book Co., 1949), p. 376.

uranium rock yields an estimate close to one billion years."[3]

One of the recent methods of dating material is that known as the carbon 14 method. Carbon 14 is a radioactive form of carbon. It is found in the atmosphere and, therefore, enters all plants and animals. All living things contain a constant amount of this carbon 14. When plants and animals die, C 14 because it is radioactive, disintegrates, and the concentration of it becomes less according to fixed laws. Therefore, by measuring the amount of C 14 left in a plant or animal it is possible to tell how long ago that organism lived and died.

There are a number of other recent and technical tests which those who work in geology, chemistry, and physics are able to use. Some of these tests can be applied to the oldest known rocks, and some apply better to the younger ones. Some tests will fit certain kinds of rocks, and some those of a different type. However, taken as a whole, such works are quite reliable and we may accept the dates for the ages of various rocks as given by even evolutionary scientists as being somewhere near that which is correct. When working with such

---

[3] Ella Thea Smith, *Exploring Biology*, 473.

large numbers, of course, even the most careful workers differ somewhat in their estimates.

Besides realizing that the earth shows abundant proof of being very old, we recognize that the various layers of rock contain very old fossils.

Some of these are of plants and animals that are now extinct. Many of these fossils show evidence of being millions of years old. There are people who explain this by saying that God might have created the earth with these fossils already formed in place. There is no doubt at all that He could have done this, but there is no evidence to support any other view than that they were formed in the usual way. Moreover, there is good reason to believe that they were formed over a long period of time, as most texts suggest.

In many places of the earth we find enormous numbers of fossils. Sometimes millions and even billions of them are found in a small area. Such an example is the diatomaceous earth found in a large quarry in the Lompoc Valley, California. Diatoms are very small plants belonging to the group we call the algae. They have an almost shell-like covering which varies in size and shape. Their beautiful patterns are revealed under the microscope. There can be no doubt that millions of them

lived in this particular area and their shells have
been dug out of these quarries by the ton. Many
interesting fossils preserved in tar have been found
in the Rancho La Brea pits in Los Angeles. Quantities of skeletons of the giant sloth, elephants,
saber-toothed tigers and many kinds of insects,
taken from these pits, can be seen in the Los Angeles County Museum of Arts and Science in Ex-
position Park in Los Angeles.

Examples of collections of numerous fossils can
be multiplied many, many times. Therefore, we
readily recognize that certain forms of life were
once much more abundant than they are at the
present time. Such abundant forms are often found
chiefly in certain layers of rocks, and so we speak
of them as being the dominant form at the time
that rock was formed. Because of the changes
found between different layers of rocks, we know
that the plants and animals which were dominant
at any one time have changed through the ages.

This brings us to the point where we should comment upon the different ages, or eras and periods,
into which the geologist divides past history. A
table giving the names and approximate duration
of each of these will be found in most biology
books. Looking down one of these tables, you will

find a period called the Cambrian. The rocks and fossils which were formed during this period are known to be millions of years old. There are several most interesting things to be noted about the fossils of this Cambrian period.

First of all, in the rocks of this period we find large quantities of fossils, but none are found in earlier strata. Some of the rocks under the Cambrian ones are of the same type. In fact, they seem to be just alike except that they contain no fossils. "The deepest and oldest layers of rock, those that date back to remote times, bear no fossil evidence of life upon the earth. Certain strata, however, near the lowest and hence nearly as old, yield fossils of primitive forms of life, such as invertebrate animals."[4] Many scientists have made long and diligent studies to try to find what we would call pre-Cambrian fossils. None have been found. The most logical explanation is that the creation of the first life took place at the beginning of the Cambrian period.

A second interesting thing to note is the absence of intermediate forms. There are "missing links" between the large groups of plants and animals

---

[4] A. O. Baker and L. H. Mills, *Dynamic Biology Today* (Rand McNally & Co., 1943), p. 628.

such as the phyla, classes and orders, and within these groups themselves. In the subject of evolution, one always hears talk of a "missing link." Usually it refers to the link between man and other animals. Many think that if that gap were bridged, evolution would be proved. It is true that this is very definitely a *missing link*, for man is *not* just one of the higher animals. He is different from all others in many ways, not only in his physical body, but also in his mental and spiritual qualities. However, this is far from being the only "missing link." There are missing ones between and within all the major plant and animal groups.

If evolution were true, we might expect to find hundreds of connecting links between the different groups, showing some of the changes which took place by which one kind of organism turned into a different kind. We should find fossils of animals and plants which would be so intermediate in their form that they could not be classified as belonging to any of our major groups. However, even the oldest fossils can be readily recognized and be assigned to the proper classification group in which they belong. We find all kinds of fossils including dragonflies, snails, corals, jellyfish, and crabs. There may be some differences, but on the whole they look very much like those same creatures today.

Of all the facts concerning the subject of evolution, this last mentioned is of primary importance. We might well expect to find that if one kind of plant or animal had ever changed into another, the evidence of this change would be found in the fossil record. This evidence is completely lacking. There is sufficient proof that change has occurred within a group as with the horse, elephant, and even man, but there is not fossil proof for believing that there has ever been change from one large classification group to another. There are some animals that have been thought by a few to bridge the chasm between some of the large groups. We will mention only one of the most notable examples, the Archaeopteryx. Some scientists say it is part reptile and part bird. Other equally good authorities, with whom we agree, say that it in no way bridges the gap between the two. Careful study of it shows it to be a bird with fully developed feathers and other bird characteristics. One of the reasons for our thinking that it is a separate and distinct animal is that there are no other animals which connect it to a reptile-like ancestry. It appears suddenly

as it is and never is found developing into anything
else.

But to get back to the fossils of the Cambrian
period. Another interesting thing about them is
their great variety. Vertebrate types are thought
by most scientists to be absent, but all of the other
large groups are found represented here. Most
books give the impression that the higher layers of
rocks contain progressively more complex fossils.
In some places this is true, and in other places
where it is not true it has been explained to be the
result of rock disturbances of various kinds. However, even in both of these cases the argument becomes ineffective because most of the fossils except
the vertebrates are also found in just this one rock
layer—that of the Cambrian period. All of the
evidence would lead us to believe that this great
variety of plants and animals found for the first
time in these rocks, was all created at about the
same time. In rocks *above* the Cambrian layer we
often do find some sort of an ascending scale of
vertebrate animals. This is to be expected as it
fits in with the creation of various kinds of living
animals on the fifth and sixth creation days.

Moreover, as these plants and animals appear in
our fossil record, all of their parts are fully formed.

Such things as arms, legs, eyes, and wings are found to be completely developed. If the theory of evolution were true, as interpreted by most people, we could expect to find these organs in various stages of development. Such stages have not been found. So we see that there are not only "missing links" in the formation of the organism as a whole, but there are also "missing links" in connection with the formation of their various parts.

Some have tried to explain away these difficulties by saying that evolution might be taking place very rapidly by great leaps and bounds. If that were the case, they say we should expect to see whole organs suddenly appearing. This does not seem to us to be a very logical conclusion even if we consider nothing other than the great complexity of some of the organs. It is not reasonable to suppose that they could be either suddenly or slowly produced by the law of chance. It seems much more reasonable to suppose that the missing links never existed and that all of our large groups of plants and animals appeared suddenly and that they appeared fully developed. We believe that this could have come about only by the creative act of God.

Chapter 4

ARGUMENT—EVOLUTION OF THE HORSE

IN GIVING PROOFS for evolution, all of our books under consideration make some mention of the horse. All of them give illustrations showing the differences between the fossil remains of an animal called Eohippus and our modern horse. Here is the story as given in *Adventures with Animals and Plants*. "As expeditions explored the rich fossil beds of Wyoming and Montana they uncovered many fossils of greater or lesser resemblance to the modern horse. The exploration is still going on but already fossils have been found that tell an astonishing story. The fossils from the various layers may be arranged in a series. In the oldest strata are found fossils of a curious small animal, *Eohippus*, which is now believed to be the ancestor of all the horses of today. It seems to have lived sixty million years ago. Until scientists found other fossils intermediate between it and the modern horse, no one would have thought of connecting Eohippus with the horse. The little Eohippus was about as big as a large cat, with four toes on the front legs and three on the back and with simple teeth that had no cement.

"In recent strata are fossils of animals like the modern horse. Between the bottom and the top are the intermediate stages. More than a hundred species have been found. Many of these are intermediate steps and fit into this series between Eohippus and the modern horse."[1]

The account in all of the books is very similar. Some give the age of Eohippus as forty-five million rather than sixty million years. Some call Eohippus a true horse and others say he was an ancestor of the true horse. It is significant to note that only one book says anything about a possible ancestor of Eohippus himself. In Hunter and Hunter we find, "The fossils of leg bones show that ages ago the remote ancestors of the horse were probably small animals, the size of a domestic cat, with five-toed feet."[2] This book then goes on with the story of

[1] Kroeber and Wolff, *Adventures with Animals and Plants*, p. 542.
[2] Hunter and Hunter, *Biology in Our Lives*, p. 408.

Eohippus with four toes on the forefeet, and three toes on the hindfeet.

REFUTATION

The story of the horse is especially interesting in view of the fact that it is used by all of our books as proof of evolution. Since all of this story concerning the horse is only change within a large group, it is not evolution at all in the sense in which the textbooks are using the word. In this booklet we will be noting several times that we have seen change in the past, are seeing it today, and still expect to see considerable change within groups in the future. We have noted the variety of men in the world today, all arising by means of known hereditary laws, from a single original pair. The same thing has been true of elephants, dogs, horses, and many other animals as well as being true of many plants.

Much study has been devoted to the horse. Great numbers of skeletons have been found. This is not a case in which conclusions are based merely on reconstructions and speculations. Moreover, while we cannot be positive about it, there seems to be good reason to believe that the series of skeletons shown in most books is reliable. This series does show an increase in size. However, this increase is no more than that which we see in the history and development of dogs. Great Danes and tiny poodles, huge St. Bernards and small Pomeranians are definitely and distinctly dogs, yet very different in size and appearance. The same is true of the horse.

Another interesting thing about the story of the horse is that there is no established record of an ancestor for Eohippus. There is no good evidence to support the statement of the one book already quoted which says that the ancestor *probably* was a five-toed creature. If this theory were true, there should be some hint as to the origin of Eohippus. None is known, for there is a gap between Eohippus and any animal which would serve as its immediate ancestor. At the present time we may conclude that it did not arise from any predecessor, but rather that it was a separately created individual.

Our whole conclusion about the horse is that it does show change. We have no way of being sure that this change means progress. However, we do know that it occurs only within a large group and is no greater than can be observed elsewhere. We start with a horse and end with a horse; therefore, it is not evolution in the true sense of the word.

Chapter 5

ARGUMENT—PROOF OFFERED FROM VESTIGIAL STRUCTURES

Vestigial structures are those parts of the body generally accepted as degenerate and useless. They are usually considered remnants left over from a useful state in some ancestral animal. Some particular gland, muscle, or bone will be pointed out as being of no use to the animal possessing it. It is claimed to have been useful once in an evolutionary predecessor. These vestigial structures are said to have degenerated during thousands of millions of years usually because of lack of use, until it is now useless and so is called "vestigial." Such organs and the number of times they are mentioned in the texts under consideration are: the appendix, 7; some scalp muscles, 3; muscles for moving the ears, 2; the coccyx bones, 3; hip bones of the whale, 4; leg bones of the python, 5; splints on the legs of the horse, 4; toe bones on the wings of birds, 3; the third eyelid, 3; and eight others mentioned at least once. Wheat and Fitzpatrick say: "There are more than two hundred vestiges in the human body. . . . These vestiges show the relationship of present forms to their remote ancestors, and, although the vestiges are useless they functioned in the earlier forms."[1]

REFUTATION

Many will be surprised at the last quotation. Very few scientists will commit themselves so far as to state that the human body has two hundred vestiges! A good many years ago such figures were used, but as we have learned more of anatomy and physiology fewer organs are labeled "vestigial." For example, the pituitary gland used to be called vestigial, but is now known to be of such prime importance that it is called the "master gland" of the body.

Most of the endocrine glands at one time or another were called useless. These facts give us our first tool to use against this general line of reasoning. Just because we do not know the function of some part of the body is no reason for stating that it is useless. Some organs that were thought for

---

[1] Wheat and Fitzpatrick, *Biology*, pp. 457, 458.

years to be useless have been found useful in the embryo. If any part functions in the developing animal, even though it may not in the adult, it cannot be called vestigial. "Our list of useless structures decreases as our store of knowledge increases."

That most of the so-called useless structures really have some function is another point to discredit the theory of evolution. Some of these organs may have minor uses, but parts of the body vary in their degree of usefulness. Some parts of the body can be amputated without too great a loss, but amputation of other more important parts would be fatal. The extent of usefulness is not the point in question.

Most of the commonly listed vestigial organs have a minor use. Our ear and scalp muscles are not developed like those of a horse, but they do give protection to underlying parts and act as "filling material." It might be noted that we do not need these muscles to be as well-developed as a horse's. A horse will use them to twitch off a fly, while we have other ways of ridding ourselves of these pests!

The coccyx, or end of the backbone, in man is also a useful structure, for some muscles that are very essential to us are attached to it.

On the inside corner of the eye is a little fold of tissue which is said to be a remnant of the third eyelid. Some reptiles have a third eyelid, so this small fold is used to link us to a reptile ancestry. We also note that this tissue is not entirely useless, for it helps to regulate the flow of tears; then, too, there has to be *some* tissue there to fill in that corner of the eye!

And what about the appendix which often causes so much trouble? The fact that it often does cause trouble is not sufficient reason to say that it is useless. This merely puts it in the class with other parts of the body which are often subject to infection. There are probably more cases of sore throat each year than there are of appendicitis, but no one would go so far as to say that the throat is vestigial and that we would be better off without it. Scientists do not agree as to the extent of usefulness of the appendix; some think that it adds lubricating fluids to the contents of the intestines; others think that it may have an endocrine function; others say it secretes small amounts of digestive juices; and still others think that it may manufacture some white blood cells. It is possible that it may have some combination of these functions, but we are sure that it is not vestigial in the true sense of the word. To this, many modern reputable scientists will agree, even though seven out of our eleven textbooks list it as a vestigial organ.

Let us next consider the so-called "hip bones" of the whale. True, there are in the whale some cartilage-like bones embedded in the flesh about where hind legs would be if a whale had legs. They are not connected with the backbone and they do not come through to the surface. We all realize that the whale is a mammal and that it possesses hair, and milk glands with which to feed its young. Since it is a mammal, it is only reasonable to believe that God created it on the same general plan that He used for other mammals. Of course, it had to be modified in various ways to fit it for a life in the water instead of on the land. In the same way the bat, another mammal, was modified to fly and was given wings instead of legs. In the whale, these "hip bones" serve a useful purpose: they support some of the internal organs and make places for the attachment of muscles.

The last of these so-called vestigial organs that we will consider is the spur-like structure on some snakes. Pythons and some other snakes have these in the region where hind legs are found in other animals. The evolutionist says that these indicate the snake once had an ancestor possessing legs. We agree that this might have been the case, but it still would not prove evolution or that one kind of animal developed into another. Even men have lost their legs through changes in the genes, those tiny structures in the nucleus of the cell. On page 401 of the third edition of L. H. Snyder's *Principles of Heredity* you will find a picture of a whole family, none of whom have legs. This condition is caused by a mutation, or change which suddenly appears and is passed on from one generation to another by the usual laws of heredity. The other thing we might say about these spurs is that, as we have seen with other so-called vestiges, they are not useless. Even though they are covered with skin, they can be used to strike a powerful blow, and in combat are often used to cut the flesh of an enemy. Some scientists also say that they are used to secure traction during locomotion.

Thinking back over this whole section, let us consider how some of these organs, which have an obscure and minor use, might have degenerated from a more perfect condition. We know that God created things perfect, for when they were finished He saw that they were good. Since sin entered the world it has caused many changes, and they have usually been toward degeneration and not improvement. Before sin had time to greatly affect the human body, man lived to be hundreds of years old. Gradually his life was shortened. This may have been due to the degenerating influence of sin. It is very possible that some of our organs now may have very different degrees of usefulness from those of Adam, Enoch, and Noah. We do not know that the appendix, lymph nodes, tonsils, etc., now have the same function as they did in early Bible times. Certainly there is some reason for a shortened life span.

Here as in other places, you will notice that several possible answers to the problem have been suggested. We may not be sure as to which is the correct solution, but we can be sure that any one of them is as logical as what the evolutionist proposes. We are also sure that every problem has an answer which is in perfect harmony with the Word of God.

Chapter 6

ARGUMENT—PROOF FROM CLASSIFICATION

ANOTHER of the so-called proofs in favor of evolution is found in the field of classification. The argument is this: As anyone looks at the plants and animals around him he observes that some are more nearly alike than others. Those that are the most alike are put into one classification group. For instance, all of the one-celled animals are put into the phylum called Protozoa. More complex animals are put into another group which is said to be "higher." The "highest" of all of the groups is said to be the Chordata. In this group we find the vertebrates, including man.

The fact that plants and animals can be classified in groups from the simple to the complex is said to be proof that they developed in the same way. It is argued that the Protozoa gave rise to the next higher animal and so on up the scale to man, who is at the top.

REFUTATION

It is interesting to note that eight of our eleven books give classification as a proof that organic evolution has taken place. But we ask, Is it any more a proof for evolution than it is for creation? In either case, we take plants and animals as we find them, and working with what is given, proceed to classify them. Those which are most alike are put into one classification group. For example, dogs are put into one and cats into another. As we have said before, similarity often does show relationship, but the question in point concerns how far this relationship can be carried. From evidence found in other fields we are led to believe that plants and animals in the same family, genera, or species may often have developed from some common ancestral type. This is the reason for many of the similarities of structure and the reason why they may well be put into the same classification group. However, the same cannot be said of the larger groups such as the phyla, classes and orders. The other reason for this similarity, as we mentioned before, is that there may have been a common plan in the mind of God when He designed them.

The fact that we can arrange the large classification groups from the simple to the complex, does not in itself show that one has developed from the other. In his work with classification, the evolutionist starts with the assumption that his theory is **true** and bases his conclusions on that assumption.

Chapter 7

ARGUMENT—PROOF
FROM GEOGRAPHIC
DISTRIBUTION

As WILL BE NOTED by referring to the chart, most of the books under consideration give a brief discussion of geographic distribution as it is related to evolution. In spite of this fact, very few of these texts actually present their arguments in concrete form. In general it seems to be similar to what is expressed by Gruenberg and Bingham: "And we rather expect a given kind of situation to maintain one kind of population and a different kind of situation to maintain a different kind of population. Yet when we examine the distribution of species over the surface of the earth, certain curious facts appear."[1] They then go on to say that regions that are very similar geograph-

[1] B. C. Gruenberg and N. E. Bingham, *Biology and Man*, (Ginn & Co., 1944), p. 460.

ically often have very different populations. Where this is true, there are usually impassable barriers between the regions. On the other hand, regions that are very different often have the same kind of populations. In this case the two regions are either directly connected or have been sometime in the past. "Facts of this kind can be explained if we assume that all organisms are derived from ancient forms, with modifications. But they cannot easily be explained in any other way."[2]

In *Basic Biology* we find a discussion about barriers separating groups of snails and chipmunks in North America. This textbook teaches that over a period of time during which these barriers existed, these snails and chipmunks developed new forms. "Deserts, mountains, forests, and other barriers isolated various groups of cottontail rabbits, which developed into a dozen kinds. Though all twelve still are cottontails, each one has a special set of characteristics which separates it from the other kinds."[3]

REFUTATION

The study of geographic distribution is both interesting and significant. We may wonder why

---

[2] Ibid., p. 463.

[3] C. L. Fenton and P. E. Kambly, *Basic Biology* (The Macmillan Company, 1947), p. 542.

kangaroos are found only in Australia, New Guinea, and adjacent islands; and why llamas are found only in South America. It takes very little discernment to observe that certain animals are found only on certain continents or parts of continents. Our problem is to explain the things we observe. How could this condition have come about?

There are several possibilities to consider. First of all there is the solution proposed by the evolutionist: where barriers existed, the species developed new forms. A second but unlikely possibility is that God might have created each of the different plants and animals as they are found in their present location. A third explanation, the best in view of our present knowledge of facts, is that God created only the large ancestral groups. From these, over long periods of time and in different places, there have developed the great variety of individual plants and animals we find today.

The tenet of the evolutionists—that isolated animals developed new forms—is not sound; it merely assumes that all of the animals of the world are related. This relationship, they say, proves a common ancestry. Making this assumption really does not help solve the problem because they start and end with an unproved theory.

Another reason that their solution is not valid is noted in the quotation from *Basic Biology*, "all of the cottontails are still cottontails." Of course differences in geographic distribution will produce differences in plants and animals. The chief question is, How much difference will environment produce?

Most of this answer must be found in the records of the past. Therefore, we will have to go back to the findings of reputable scientists who have worked with rocks and their fossils. They have found, suddenly appearing in the rock record, representatives of practically all of our major groups—that is, at least phyla, classes and orders. Between these there are missing links, a fact which gives us every reason to believe that they must have been special creations. On the other hand, some of the families, genera, and species seem to have arisen from these specially created large groups. All will agree that environment and geographical location played a part in this change. Therefore our disagreement with the evolutionist is in the amount of variation that can be produced by geographic locations and conditions.

Two other factors which enter into this picture are mutations and selection. By mutations we mean unusual changes which suddenly appear. Because these are caused by a change within the nucleus of a cell, such changes can be passed on to succeeding generations.

The following is an example of the way in which selections and mutations might operate to produce some of the conditions we note in connection with the geographic distribution of living things. If a mutation in the form of a white fur-bearing animal were produced in temperate regions, it would be so conspicuous that probably it would be quickly killed. If, however, such a mutation occurred in a snow-covered region, it would be more likely to survive than its darker-colored relatives.

It is very possible that in this way various groups of animals have been developed and are now found in environments in which they are especially fitted to live. Entirely aside from evolution this would explain some of the things we observe in connection with geographic distributions.

Chapter 8

ARGUMENT—PROOF FROM EMBRYOLOGY

Many of the old so-called proofs from the field of embryology are still being taught. Seven of the books surveyed call attention to the fact that there is a similarity between embryos, especially in their early stages. This quotation from Kroeber and Wolff is typical: "One of the most interesting things about vertebrates is that the embryos of all of them are so much alike. . . .These similarities do not seem strange if we assume that all vertebrates are descendants of a common ancestor. If they are related to each other, it is not surprising that their development should be similar."[1] Six of the books under consideration give a chart much like the original one compiled by Haeckel picturing the various embryos and the likenesses between them.

---

[1] Kroeber and Wolff, *Adventures with Animals and Plants*, pp. 548, 550.

In this field it is also claimed that some animals in their embryological development pass through some of the same stages that the race is supposed to have gone through in its evolutionary history. In other words, it is said that the development of an individual parallels that of the race. This has been called the recapitulation theory. In the past, many books have included the one-cell, the gill slit, the tail, and the hair stages. They say that all human embryos now start life as a single cell, and that this is a picture of the time, millions of years ago, when all life started from a one-celled animal, a protozoa. *Biology in Our Lives* presents the gill-slit argument in typical style. "The relationship between a human embryo and embryos of lower vertebrates is indicated by the presence of a series of narrow slits in the neck region of all vertebrate embryos. These clefts correspond in number and position to the so-called gill slits of certain fish, such as the shark."[2] The claim that human embryos have a tail is used as proof that these descended from animals having tails. The same thing was once said of a hair stage, linking us to a hairy ancestor; but that has now been dropped from most books and is not mentioned in the ones listed for our consideration.

---

[2] Hunter and Hunter, *Biology in Our Lives*, p. 414.

REFUTATION

If there is any one field of biology where we can see at work supernatural creative power rather than materialistic evolution, it is here in embryology. He is truly a miraculous God who can cause a single egg cell to develop into a complex animal. From that single cell come all different kinds of tissues, organs, and systems. Not only are they different in their structure but they are different as to function. Muscle tissues develop with the power of contracting, whereas nerve tissue develops with the ability to carry impulses. The Psalmist has said, "I am fearfully and wonderfully made." It seems strange that this marvelous process in which we see the wonder of God so beautifully portrayed should be the one concerning which the evolutionist interprets the facts in his own special way to try to prove his dogma. A brief consideration will show the fallacies of the line of reasoning concerning embryology.

First, consider the fact that there is a resemblance between embryos. Some of this original work was done by Ernst Haeckel. He made a series of diagrams of different embryos and demonstrated that they had certain characteristics in common. Later he admitted that some of his drawings had been intentionally changed to make them fit the theory he was trying to prove. It is said that when Haeckel was confronted with the fact that some of his drawings were not true to life he said that he would feel condemned by admitting the fact were it not that many other scientists had also doctored, schematized and reconstructed their drawings. It would seem as though he were exaggerating in his wholesale condemnation of other scientists, but he surely should be able to speak for himself.

That there are some similarities between the embryos, especially in early stages, all will admit. Our only disagreement is with the degree of similarity and with the interpretation. The degree of likeness is not nearly so striking as the textbook illustrations would suggest. Ever since Haeckel's original schematized drawings, books have continued to print similar pictures showing various embryos all about the same size and curvature. If a student had before him the original embryos instead of the diagrams, he would be able to see more differences than the pictures show.

However, there are likenesses. But some of those noted by evolutionists are only superficial: in spite of the apparent similarities, each embryo invariably develops into the kind of individual from whose egg it came. Chicken eggs develop into chickens, and frog eggs develop into frogs.

The real likenesses can be attributed, as in the adult, to the fact that the Maker followed a general plan, with modifications, to fit the particular need of each animal. As was pointed out in connection with similarities of adults, similarities among embryos might just point to a common plan in the mind of God.

The proposition that the human individual begins life as a one-celled protozoan is entirely fallacious. It begins life as a fertilized human ovum, or egg, which is very different in structure and function from a one-celled animal. This fertilized ovum is capable of developing into a new individual, but it can neither reproduce itself nor carry on many of the life processes that are found in the protozoan. Therefore, there is no basis whatever for accepting this part of the recapitulation theory.

The concept of the gill-slit stage is equally misleading. A few years ago many of the books discussed the "gills" of the human embryo. However, this idea is so obviously false that the teaching now usually refers to the "gill-slits" only. As an embryo develops, there are ridges that grow in from the sides and develop into parts of the tongue, lower jaw and neck. While there are folds in between these ridges, they do not normally break through into the pharynx and so are not comparable to the beginnings of gill slits.

The teaching concerning the human embryo having a tail has been so obviously falsified in the past that it has fallen into disrepute, and now most books wisely omit any reference to it. The hair stage is now also usually omitted. The tail stage is mentioned twice in our books. There is one mention of it in Kroeber and Wolff. "For a considerable time, too, the human embryo has a tail. This region stops growing at an early stage, and as the embryo gets larger the tail becomes less and less evident. A few small bones remain as the the the coccyx."[3]

Instead of really talking about a tail, the author is discussing the coccyx, or end part of the backbone. To be a tail, a structure must be a caudal appendage having its own muscles, nerves, and blood supply. The coccyx, found in the human embryo, is not a separate and distinct structure having the above characteristics, but is merely the terminal portion of the backbone. After all, it does have to have an end! At no time in its development does it have more than the normal thirty-

[3] Kroeber and Wolff, *Adventures with Animals and Plants*, p. 548.

three vertebrae. It is true that at one time it does project beyond the surrounding parts because they have different rates of growth, but that never makes it anything other than the end of the backbone.

There are several unanswered questions in this whole line of reasoning. First, if the developing embryo is supposed to re-enact the stages in the evolutionary history of the race, why are so few stages included? Why should we find some of them appearing in the wrong order? Why should we not find thousands of steps, rather than only a few? Why does the embryo go through some steps that could not possibly have been included in the evolutionary history of the animal? How can such stages as the egg, larva, pupa, and adult stages of a butterfly be explained? Why do only some parts of the embryo show recapitulation and other parts never show it?

Could it be that the scientists are merely trying to prove a preconceived theory? If this is the case, and it seems to be, they are in the field of speculation, not true science. True science looks at all facts impartially. Some have said that the recapitulation theory is merely a deduction from the main dogma of evolution. Since the recapitulation theory has not been proved, it cannot be used as proof of the main theory of evolution.

Chapter 9

ARGUMENT—EVOLUTION
OF MAN

WE ARE NOW READY to consider very briefly what is being presented today about the evolution of man. We find that the youth of our country are being taught many things that are anti-Biblical as well as anti-scientific. Some of the teaching no longer accepted by the best scientists is being carried along in texts as it has been for the past thirty, forty, or fifty years. Many of these teachings are based on facts which are sometimes incorrectly interpreted. When starting the study of the origin of man, it is especially easy to assume that evolution is a fact, instead of beginning with an open mind to see what the facts really show. Here are some samples of the teaching that is being presented. E. T. Smith says: "The fossil record is good evidence that man himself *did not appear suddenly* on the earth in his present form but has gradually developed from a much more primitive species. What species gave rise to modern man has not yet been proved, but biologists agree that man, like other animals, arose not suddenly in his modern form, but by a gradual series of changes in some pre-existing primitive species through a period of from one to two million years."[1]

In Gruenberg's book there is an interesting account of the evolution of man. By careful reading you will find that the author commits himself much further than most scientists on the subject of the "missing link." "At the close of the last century thinking people were discussing the evolutionary theory as applied to man. Many who were willing to assume that evolution had taken place among plants and lower animals hesitated to accept the same explanation for the appearance of man upon the earth. One of the strongest arguments urged against the theory was the fact that it had been impossible to produce a complete record of a graded series connecting men of today with his supposed nonhuman or prehuman ancestors.

"This argument of the 'missing link' carried a great deal of weight. For most people do not appreciate how unlikely it would be for a complete

[1] Ella Thea Smith, *Exploring Biology*, p. 485.

series of specimens to be preserved through the far-reaching changes which the earth itself has undergone. Of the millions of human beings and other vertebrates that die in a given region during a century, how many skeletons are likely to remain sufficiently intact to be recognized from ten to fifty thousand years later? From a scientific point of view, it would be sufficient if the scattered pieces found at widely different levels (geological ages) did actually fit in with a *supposed* series.

"The few bones found in Java in the early eighteen nineties by the Dutch army surgeon, Eugene Dubois (1858-1940,) fit into such a series in a very satisfactory way. The type of animal to which these bones belong is named *Pithecanthropus erectus*, and probably represents a 'missing link.' "[2]

REFUTATION

Are there really fossils of ancient man which show an ascending scale from the lower animals up to modern man? Is there in existence such a thing as a "missing link" that can connect man with a lower, beastlike ancestry?

One of the most interesting helps in answering

---

[2] Gruenberg and Bingham, *Biology and Man*, p. 515.

these questions are the reconstructions. These are cases of plaster of Paris figures of the entire man built from a few bones, or even part of a bone. Museums and textbooks contain many such pictures and exhibits. The average man takes these at face value without realizing that a great portion of such pictures and exhibits is imaginary. Hence, the man who starts with the assumption that evolution is true is likely to make his reconstructions with thick necks, hairy bodies, beastlike faces, a stooped position, and a general apelike form.

In various books there are some interesting stories showing the extremes to which reconstructions have been carried. Some cases are humorous, but they surely are not the average work of careful scientists. Moreover, much of the reconstruction done by careful workers is admittedly tentative or temporary. Unfortunately when such work was transferred to textbooks, the reservations were often omitted. As a result, some of the pictures and descriptions found in the texts are more reconstruction than fact. The original Java man was reconstructed from a skull cap, a left femur, a piece of jaw, and three teeth. Since these first skeletal remains were found, parts of four more skulls, another lower jaw, an upper jaw, and a few long bones have been found. However, one author wisely suggests, "Caution must be observed in generalizing from these very few fossils."[3]

The Heidelberg man as pictured in many books appears to be part beast and part man. His form was entirely reconstructed from one lower jaw!

The Piltdown man was reconstructed from skull fragments and most of a lower jaw. One book stated, "The Piltdown skull has puzzled scientists."[4] This is putting it mildly! They could not agree among themselves as to how the fragments should be put together. Some well-trained men have reconstructed the Piltdown skull to be about the size of the average head of today. Other equally reputable men place the skull fragments closer together so that the result is a much smaller head. This smaller one is said to belong to a more primitive, less intelligent individual. We say that it takes very little observation to discover that head size and intelligence do not always go together!

The extremes in reconstruction are not all confined to the past. In the March 21, 1949, copy of *Life* magazine, several pages were devoted to reconstructions in "A New Giant Appears on Man's

[3] Wheat and Fitzpatrick, *Biology*, p. 444.
[4] Ibid., p. 443.

Family Tree." In this story of Dr. Broom's search for fossils in South Africa, there is a half-page picture of a bestial-looking face, with the caption, "The biggest ape-man as reconstructed by discoverer Broom has an enormous face but a small brain. Broom guesses at hair, lips, ear." A careful reading of the article shows that the only thing Dr. Broom discovered was a jaw fragment with four teeth. From that, in his reconstruction Dr. Broom guessed not only at the hair, lips and ear, but at all the rest of the apelike face and head as well. In the same article we also find, "[This reconstructed animal] helps bridge the still wide gap between man and the earliest apelike creatures from which he rose." Periodic literature continually contains material on this subject. In the March 1952, copy of *Science Digest* we find an article about "An ape's skull 30,000,000 years old . . . throwing new light on man's ancestry." There has been much publicity concerning the recent finds of the Hotu man in the limestone caves of northeastern Iran. Many scientific magazines have carried accounts of these findings. Again we have a case of assuming the result from the beginning. The reconstruction is made to fit into the theory already advanced.

True, a scientist who knows his field *can* tell much about a whole body from its parts. However, in the past even careful and accurate reconstruction has come into disrepute. Reconstruction has been carried so far that it has passed from true science into pure guesswork. In your studies, watch carefully and see if you can tell the difference between results based on scientific investigation and mere guesswork.

The evangelical Christian should be advised to be careful in discrediting *all* work of reconstruction. Many other fossils have been found that are complete skeletons. Unfortunately many of our high school texts continue to list these early and incomplete finds. From these remnants, and from the more complete finds like the Peking and Cro-Magnon man, there are several facts which we should acknowledge. One of these is the great age of some of the fossils of true men. There is every reason to believe that many of them are much older than had formerly been thought possible by Bible scholars. If all of the fossils now being found do not fit in with the 4004 B.C. chronology for Genesis as given by Ussher, we do not need to be disturbed. There is one thing of which we may be sure: The God who created this world is the same

One who wrote the account of the creation; there can be no conflict between the Word and the works. If there is a seeming contradiction between the Bible and the findings of science, it is only because we do not have a full knowledge of all the facts in the case. Added research and study may reveal some of these, but some of them may not be fully understood until we reach Heaven, when all things will be made plain.

We can be very emphatic about the fact that there is no graded series of connecting links between man and the lower animals. Some of the oldest fossils are admittedly different from modern man, but there is no evidence that any of them are anything but human. Some of the early forms of humans looked somewhat different from any known form on the earth today. Some of them have ridges and depressions and a general shape different from living forms. Some have a heavier bony structure. Again, *some* of the earliest fossils cannot be told from modern ones. Some people foolishly contend that there are forms living today as strange as any of the fossils of man that have ever been found. This is not true, because there are actually differences between modern men and some of the early fossil forms. But all of these early ones are unmistakably human; there is no basis at all for calling any of them a "missing link."

As we have said, some of the fossils of men are what we might call a primitive type, but some of these are not chronologically the oldest. Some of the oldest are much like those living today. The evolutionist often disregards the fact that if we arrange our fossils of men according to their age, their shape and structure does not then fit in with the evolution theory. If in turn we arrange their shape and structure to fit the theory, then they are no longer arranged from the youngest to the oldest. It is interesting to note that in the past some have taught that man not only does not show evolution, but that he shows the opposite—degeneration. This is said of both his physical body and of his culture, or non-inherited activities. The outstanding example given to support degeneration in his physical form is comparison of modern man with the Cro-Magnon man. Here is a description of him.

"In 1868, at Cro-Magnon, France, the first five skeletons of men that lived twenty-five thousand years ago were discovered. Soon, eighty-two skeletons of individuals of this race had been found; and, now, many more than a hundred skeletons of these apparently athletic men averaging about six feet in height, are matters of record. The skull indicates that the heads of these men were long and narrow, and the foreheads were high, shapely, and not retreating. The lower jaws were strong, with a shortened, firm, well-developed chin. The brain was large, and the implements and art found with the skeletons indicate that these people were intelligent and had a high stage of culture. They made elaborate tools of flint, horn and bone, which were used for hunting, sewing, and preparing skins for clothing. They carved and painted figures of many different animals on bone and horn and on the walls of caves. Their pictures show the methods of hunting, which include the use of the javelin, the bow and arrow, and the harpoon, and the construction of traps. They had a well-organized religion and seem to have had a belief in a future life. These intelligent Cro-Magnon men were probably responsible for the extermination of the slow-witted Neanderthalers."[5]

These statements about Cro-Magnon men are neither imaginary nor are they misinterpretations to fit any special theory. Such a group of people really lived and possessed the characteristics usually attributed to them. However, as Christians, we

[5] Wheat and Fitzpatrick, *Biology*, pp. 446, 447.

should be just as careful in our interpretation as we want the evolutionist to be in his. Such a small group of people confined to such a small area is a definite exception to the rule. We are not justified in using it as the basis of any over-all generalization in either the direction of evolution or degeneration. In this field it is a temptation to draw conclusions from too little evidence. In fact, if at some future time similar work were being done in the study of the men of today and such small samplings were used, the work might well be discredited.

As to his culture, some say man has degenerated because certain arts and skills, such as the Pyramid and Sphinx building of the Egyptians, as well as their stained glass and their embalming of mummies, after reaching a high degree of development have been practically lost for centuries. The same thing is true of other ancient civilizations; we often find a less specialized one replacing a more advanced civilization. But again, while these things are true they are the exceptions. Taken as a whole, the picture of man has been one of general progress, greater complexity and increased specialization. This should not be confused with evolution as we are using the word. In no way does it show that man has developed from lower animals or that he is now changing into anything other than man. We should not be guilty of refusing to admit progress or of confusing it with organic evolution.

Let us now sum up what we have so briefly considered concerning the evolution of man. Believing that all in the world today are descended from Adam and Eve, we see that there has been some change. In considering this change we have seen that we should use care in distinguishing between reconstructions and the interpretation of them, and other complete fossil finds. Scientists agree that there is only one genus of man living on the earth today, genus Homo. We recognize the fact that there have never been any fossils found which show evidence that any men have ever lived that were anything other than Homo. There is no graded series from beastlike creatures to man. There is not even one link in such a supposed series. We find very old fossils, some of which lie very deep in undisturbed rock, but they are still human. We can arrive at no other conclusion than that man appeared suddenly on the earth in a form not too different from what we find today.

Although we do not know *when* it took place and we do not know the details as to *how* it took place, we still have every reason to accept at face value the Genesis account of the origin of man. "Then

God said, Let us make man in our image. . . . So
God created man in his own image, in the image
of God created he him; male and female created
he them" (Gen. 1:26, 27).

Are you not glad that you were created in the
image of God instead of being some higher form of
a beastlike creature? The phrase "created in his
image," we know refers to our soul and spirit
rather than to our body. We are glad that He has
given us mental and spiritual capacities that are
not possessed by any other living creature. Between man and these lower creatures there exists,
and apparently has always existed, a great un-
bridged gap. How wonderful that He has given us
the ability to comprehend His Word! Through acceptance of His plan for our salvation we rejoice
that we can enter into a place of fellowship and
communion with the One who created the world
and then made us new creations in Him.

Chapter 10

ORIGIN OF LIFE

Now that we have looked at the chief reasons given by the majority of our books as proofs of evolution, let us consider some of the things which most of the texts do not mention. One of these vital points concerns the origin of life. Some evolutionist is likely to say, "The origin does not concern us, we merely take the beginning by faith and then try to account for the way by which life developed." However, if a person's theory of development is to be reasonable, it will not preclude a reasonable explanation concerning the *beginning* of that development. In the past as well as in the present, some evolutionists have frankly said that they cannot accept anything which is supernatural or which involves a miracle. As one of our books says, "Nor will most scientists admit that life has 'always' existed on the earth or that it came into being through a 'miracle'."[1] This position is typi-

---

[1] Gruenberg and Bingham, *Biology and Man*, p. 443.

cal of the natural man whose mind is darkened to spiritual things so that he cannot understand them. When that person starts with the assumption that there is no God capable of creating various forms of life, he must explain the variety that exists in some other way. This he has done in his theory of evolution. Whether or not this theory concerns the beginning of life, we must consider the beginning to get a whole picture of the situation. If God and miracles have been ruled out, then how can the origin of life be explained? The only other possibility is what we call spontaneous generation, or the origin of life from non-living material. Before the work of many great scientists, especially of Redi in the seventeenth century and of Pasteur in the nineteenth, this belief was common. However, spontaneous generation has now been so thoroughly disproved that *Webster's Collegiate Dictionary* (Sixth edition) reads, "from a belief, now abandoned." There is no better accepted principle in science today than "Life comes from life."

Many men have spent a lifetime in the laboratory trying to create life. Protoplasm has been analyzed to find exactly what proportion of the various elements it contains. These same proportions are then combined, but no life results. Even the best scientific minds of today, working with the best equipment available and under ideal conditions, are not able to produce life. Yet this same process is said to have happened in the past just by the chance coming together of elements on a barren earth devoid of all living things. This theory is the only alternative to belief in creation, and yet many evolutionists will not believe in creation. They admit that the situation leaves them in a dilemma. Gruenberg and Bingham's thirteen-page account of the various theories concerning the origin of life is an interesting one. They conclude it with a paragraph entitled, "The Scientist's Dilemma," in which they say: "Scientists reject the sun myths and ocean myths of ancient times. They treat modern tales of 'spontaneous' transformation of rubbish and dirty water into worms or mice as examples of false inference or of faulty observation. Nor will most scientists admit that life has 'always' existed on the earth or that it came into being through a 'miracle.' That is, we cannot admit, that there has ever been any violation of those orderly relationships between substances and forces which we call the 'laws of nature'. Nevertheless, scientists are obliged to assume that life originated from nonliving matter. Life did and still does so originate."[2] To get out of the dilemma, men will believe in the unscientific process of spontaneous generation rather than admit that God has performed miracles.

Recent research has produced materials that behave somewhat like a virus, and some scientists hold the belief that in the future, living material will actually be produced from nonliving elements. The question will arise in the minds of some: "If life ever *is* produced in a test tube, will that prove evolution?" Someone has said that it would rather prove that a very superior mind is needed to make living material. It is something that could not have happened by the law of chance.

However, if such a thing did happen in the past, what did the first cell have for food? One of our books says that the first life was probably some bacteria-like form. If it was, it did not possess chlorophyll and would have been dependent for its food supply on other organic sources. But there would have been no such sources, and so the first frail living cell would have starved to death! Maybe we are wrong in saying that it was frail. *Biology for Better Living* indicates that it must have been very hardy indeed: "Probably very simple, it was

[2] Gruenberg and Bingham, *Biology and Man*, p. 443.

a pioneer form of life that could stand the extremes of light and darkness, drought and moisture, and unbalanced food supply that were provided on these uncertain homesteads."[2]

To us it is impossible to conceive of life coming into being and continuing to exist without the all-powerful hand of God. It is a miracle which we take by faith.

[2] E. E. Bayles and R. W. Burnett, *Biology for Better Living* (Silver Burdett Co., 1946), p. 60.

Chapter 11

ORIGIN OF MATTER

THE BODY of teaching connected with the theory of evolution not only offers no explanation for the origin of life, but it gives none for the origin of matter. Many high school books give some kind of account of the origin of the earth such as the now outdated one that the earth flew off the sun. Others, such as Wheat and Fitzpatrick give an account like the following: "One theory of the beginning of the earth suggests that a whirling mass of material grew by attracting other solid particles, maybe small planets, which filled the surrounding area. With the change in size, the gravity of the earth increased and a compressed interior core gave rise to heat" (p. 409). Explanations such as this do not in any way account for the real origin of matter. When the evolutionist asks the Christian for his explanation, several verses can be quoted: "By the word of the Lord the heavens were made; and all the host of them by the breath of his mouth . . .

For he spake, and it was done; he commanded, and it stood fast" (Ps. 33:6, 9).

Some years ago the Christian was laughed at for believing that all matter in the universe could be made from "nothing." He had to answer, "I don't know how it was done; but it is in the Bible, so I take it by faith and believe it." That is the attitude we should take toward God's Word. As Christians have done this down through the ages, their faith has often been turned to sight as truths from the Bible have been revealed. That is what happened early in this twentieth century concerning the knowledge we have of the origin of matter.

As the study of physics took rapid strides forward, we learned more and more about the structure of molecules and atoms. We are told that atoms are made up largely of negative and positive charges of electricity. In other words, matter is made up of energy and power. The Christian is not surprised; he reminds his opponents that he has always believed that God created by the power of His might. Outside the Christian viewpoint there is no logical and scientifically sound way of accounting for the beginning of the universe. The only reasonable solution is to believe the Word as it stands.

Chapter 12

TIME OF CREATION

As THIS BOOK has been read, various questions concerning creation may have come to mind. Two of the chief ones are (1) When did creation take place? and (2) How long did the actual work of creation take? In the ranks of orthodox Christians it is easy to find sincere people who hold very different views concerning these questions. It is not our object here to discuss these various theories. We will merely mention three of them. Much has been written about each, both favorable and unfavorable. It would be well to read some of these books.[1]

In some books you will find a discussion of the possibility that a long period of time existed between Genesis 1:1 and 1:2. Various authors propose the theory that there was an original creation which was destroyed by a cataclysmic event; re-

---

[1] Members of the American Scientific Affiliation, *Modern Science and Christian Faith*. Wheaton, Ill.: Van Kampen Press, 1950.

creation took place in six literal days.[2] There is also the theory that creation took place in six days of time about four thousand years ago. Other writers offer a different answer to the question of the age of the earth; they say that the creative "days" may have been long periods of time.

Anyone who is interested in the subject should secure writings on the various theories and study them with an open mind. First and foremost, of course, should be the study of God's Word. A superficial reading is not enough, for it should be studied as by a "workman who has no need to be ashamed" (see II Tim. 2:15). The things which He has created should be studied with equal thoroughness. We will not immediately find all the answers we are seeking, but we can be sure that the Bible and true science will never contradict each other.

---

[2] L. Allen Higley, *Science and Truth.* New York: Fleming H. Revell Company, 1940.

Chapter 13

A RUNNING-DOWN
PROCESS

THE THEORY of evolution teaches that over a long period of time things have been building up to greater and greater complexity. "In the preceding problem you have learned many reasons for believing that . . . the first animals and plants that appeared on the earth were simple and that they have given rise throughout the ages to more complex forms."[1]

We honestly ask, "It this what we observe in the things we see around us? Are things in general being built up, or are they wearing out?"

Most people will agree that we commonly observe just the opposite of the evolutionary building-up process. The sun is being consumed so that it is slowly cooling off. Its energy and other energy

[1] Kroeber and Wolff, *Adventures with Animals and Plants*, p. 555.

in the universe is being lost as far as our use of it is concerned. As energy is given off, the source of that energy must become disintegrated. Following this back to the beginning, there must have been a time when there was a very high degree of organization. This could be none other than "in the beginning [when] God created the heaven and the earth." The whole picture of our universe, with very few exceptions, is a running-down, slowing-up, wearing-out process.[2]

---

[2] Robert E. D. Clark, *Darwin Before and After* (The Paternoster Press, 1948), chap. 8.

Chapter 14

POSSIBLE METHODS OF EVOLUTION

I F EVOLUTION is true, there must be some method by which it could have come about. Remember now, we are not talking about the origin of species. We will comment a little later on how this has happened and continues to take place.

Here we are talking about the origin of larger groups such as the phyla, classes and orders. Our problem concerns this question: Is there any known way, aside from special creation, that these larger groups could have come into existence, or that one could develop into another?

Referring to our texts, we find that many of them discuss the various theories for the way evolution might have taken place. Some of the books point out the weaknesses of these theories. However, since all of them do not, we will briefly mention the weakness of the most important theories which were proposed by Dr. Lamarck, Darwin and De Vries.

Lamarck's theory concerns the inheritance of acquired characteristics. "Lamarck knew that the muscles of a blacksmith's right arm grow larger and more powerful with use. He knew, too, that an arm bound in a splint shrinks in size through disuse. Lamarck decided that the use of any particular organ continued through successive generations would develop it and thus change it. . . . He thought giraffe ancestors stretched their necks to reach the higher parts of the tree. After many generations of such stretching, the long-necked giraffe was evolved."[1]

"This use and disuse theory would be a lovely theory, if it were true. The flaw in it may be evident to you. The difficulty with it is that acquired characteristics do not seem to be inherited, as you have already learned. A blacksmith's son does not inherit his father's big right arm. Cutting off dog's tails or trimming their ears does not cause them to have puppies with changed traits. . . . Obviously this theory cannot be accepted as the true explanation of evolution."[2]

---

[1] Ella Thea Smith, *Exploring Biology*, p. 491.
[2] Ella Thea Smith, p. 492.

Darwin's theory is characterized by the phrases, "struggle for existence" and "survival of the fittest." He said that we see living things contending with each other for food and the necessities of life. In this struggle the weak die off and the strong ones live. The total effect he pictured as resulting in stronger and better plants and animals.

There are several points to criticize in Darwin's theory. First of all, there are many situations in nature where no struggle for existence is found. Secondly, the fittest are not nearly always the ones to survive. Thirdly, where these two conditions are found and better individuals are produced, they are still the same kind of individuals.

"Survival, however, merely separates the strong from the weak, the fit from the unfit. New species could not be formed by survival alone. Darwin did not have our modern knowledge of heredity, and his theory could not explain how changes are passed on to succeeding generations."[3]

Mutations is the key word of the DeVries theory. "We can define a mutation as a change in the structure or composition of the gene which is heritable."[4] These changes produce plants and animals which

---

[3] Hunter and Hunter, *Biology in Our Lives*, p. 418.
[4] Vance and Miller, *Biology for You*, p. 549.

are often radically different from their parents. Some of the most common examples of famous mutations in the past are the seedless orange, the short-legged Ancon sheep and hornless cattle. The chief argument against using the DeVries theory to account for the way evolution could have taken place, is found in the fact that most mutations are harmful rather than helpful. This, of course, is looking at the situation from the viewpoint of the plant or animal involved and not from that of man. If the Ancon ram had not been protected by man it would have fallen prey to its speedier enemies because its short legs handicapped it in running and jumping. Hornless cattle, in the same way, have lost one of their best means of protecting themselves against their enemies. The seedless orange, although beneficial to man, would have been fatal to the continued existence of that plant. The same is true of one of the mutations of the evening primrose which produced only female offspring. In fruit flies most of the mutations cause harmful conditions such as deformed wings and legs, absence of eyes, reduction of the area of vision of the eye or of the amount of pigment in it.

Although most mutations are harmful to the individual producing them, we have to recognize the fact that some few are beneficial. The evolutionist says, "By the method of natural selection organisms having helpful mutations are preserved and produce new kinds of offspring."

Because this idea is found in many of our books, we should give it a little more consideration. They say it is easy to see how mutations and natural selection working together could account for evolution. It is by no means easy. First of all, mutations are of far too infrequent occurrence to explain the whole process of evolution. Then, too, they do not all take place in the same direction. In fact it is very hard to see how they expand in all directions to produce the great variety of plants and animals we see today, and at the same time concentrate their efforts toward a central point such as that of producing a complex organ like the eye.

Then, too, we should consider whether the changes by mutation could ever account for all living things having come from one original cell. Some scientists have said that many small mutations, if they ever could be beneficial and work in the same direction of increasing complexity, would account for this. Others have said that evolution would have to take place by a smaller number of large mutations. Neither of these explanations is satisfactory. Mutations, either small or large, do produce changes. However, these changes are all within large groups. They are never great enough to account for the origin of new phyla, classes, or orders. These groups seem to have existed from the beginning in their present distinct forms.

Recent work in the field of heredity should give us some light on ways other than mutation by which changes occur.

One of the most familiar ways is by a recombination of characteristics which results in hybrids. We commonly see children who have inherited some traits from each of their parents. Most of our domesticated plants and animals are the result of such hybridization. New and better ones are still being produced by this method. However, even if it is carefully controlled by man, such change is very limited. This takes place only within small groups. If we cross individuals which are very different, we soon run into a blind alley because the resulting hybrids will be sterile. This is because each group of living things has its own definite number of chromosomes within the nucleus of its particular cells. If an egg is fertilized by a

sperm which has a different number of chromosomes, sterile, abnormal individuals are produced,
because the chromosomes cannot come together in
pairs as they ordinarily do. For example, an egg
having twenty chromosomes is not compatible with
a sperm having only sixteen. It is therefore, impossible to produce an unlimited number of changes
by developing hybrids.

Some limited change can also be produced by
changing the numbers of chromosomes. Sometimes
chromosomes break apart and become fastened together again in a different way. Sometimes a piece
of one will even become fastened to another. We
see these various methods being used today, as in
the past, to give us new varieties and even species.
All of these methods will produce a change, but
none of them produce any change great enough to
cause evolution. It is here in this study of heredity
that we should find some clue as to how it could
have taken place. Our present stock of knowledge
leaves us with no known method by which evolution could have come about. More will be learned
in the future, but enough research has already been
done that if any such method existed we would
at least have found some clue as to what that method

is. Lacking this clue, we may logically come back again to the conclusions that evolution is not a fact and that "In the beginning God *created* . . . " (Gen. 1:1.

Chapter 15

NUMBER OF CHROMOSOMES

ANOTHER INTERESTING thing in connection with chromosomes has to do with the number we find in different plants and animals. Since the chromosomes are responsible for the characteristics which are inherited, it is logical to suppose that their number would be less in the simple organisms and more in the complex ones. If evolution were true, might we not expect to see new chromosomes added as we ascend the plant and animal scale? This is surely not the case.

The following groups are arranged approximately in order as they are said to have evolved. We certainly do not see a general increase in chromosome number to correspond with the general increase in complexity.

---

[1] Baker and Mills, *Dynamic Biology Today*, p. 590; Ella Thea Smith, *Exploring Biology*, p. 140.

Name of some plants	Chromosomes in body cells
An alga	48
Another alga	24
A moss	40
Bracken fern	64
Pine	24
Onion	16
A lily	48
Wheat	20
Peas	14
Name of some animals	
Earthworm	32
A snail	48
A crayfish	208
A housefly	12
Trout	24
Chicken	18
Horse	60
Cattle	16
Man	48

The question is often asked, "If evolution is true, why do simple forms of life still exist today?" According to the theory of evolution, new forms of life appeared over long periods of time and survived because they were better fitted to live in a particular environment. If these new plants and animals were better fitted to live, why did not the less fit gradually become extinct? The answer is found in the fact that they are not less fit. As far as we can tell, such simple things as bacteria and protozoa have been in existence from the time life first came into being. The fact that we still have these same simple forms shows that they are well fitted to live in their particular environment. If they had ever been the only living things in the world there is no reason why they ever should have evolved into anything different. There is no reason why evolution should have taken place.

Chapter 16

DESIGN IN NATURE

IT IS EVIDENT to the student that design runs like a thread through all of the sciences. It does not matter to which one of them we look, we see design according to a definite plan. We find it in physics and in biology. We see order and planning in astronomy and chemistry. The organization within a molecule shows a precision that cannot be duplicated by man. The more we magnify and enlarge the things of nature, the more evident is the design. This certainly cannot be said of the things which are made by man. His works are essentially different from the things which God has created.

"The heavens declare the glory of God, and the firmament showeth his handiwork" (Ps. 19:1). Such order and precision as we see in the universe around us could not come into existence by itself. Behind it all there must have been a mind, and a mind greater than that of man.

As we look at the human body we realize the truth of Psalm 139:14 that it is "fearfully and wonderfully made." Even though the human body shows corruption and lack of perfection, it still has a marvelous complexity that demands an intelligent Maker. The Bible clearly tells us that God created it and its parts. "He that planted the ear, shall he not hear? he that formed the eye, shall he not see?" (Ps. 94:9).

When we consider the body as a whole, we realize that it could not have come into existence by the ordinary working of the laws of science which we see around us every day. If we take only a part of it, such as the nervous system, we still find order and planning. If we examine only a small organ of that system, such as the eye, our wonder increases. As we study the cells that make up that organ we are amazed at their diversity and perfection. As we consider the molecular and atomic structures within those cells, we see not the happenings of luck and chance, but rather the planning of a master mind.

In the instincts of the wild animals around us we notice a different kind of design in the plan of God. Aside from creation, there is no satisfactory way to explain their complex behavior. As we consider how birds migrate and the complicated, characteristic nests they build, we realize that they could not have come about by a gradual evolutionary process. In order to be useful, such instincts must have come into being in an already perfect form. Such things do not happen by chance. They are the result of foresight and planning. The chance that our planet could spontaneously arise by itself with all of the features necessary for life, and then that life itself just "happened" to come into existence, is a statistical monstrosity. Behind it all is a mind, the mind of God who created the universe. "The sea is his, for he made it: and his hands formed the dry land" (Ps. 95:5).

Chapter 17

THEISTIC EVOLUTION

Someone is likely to say, "Can I not believe in both the Bible and evolution? Couldn't God have created the very first life and then all living things have evolved from that?" This might seem like an easy solution to a vexing problem, and the enemy of our souls would have us answer "Yes." But, the real answer is an unqualified and emphatic "No."

Some of the high school texts we have been considering carry an idea like this: "There is nothing in science which is opposed to a belief in God and religion. Those who think so are mistaken either in their science or their theology or both."[1] Now, of course, this should be true. We would even go farther and say that it *is* true if one is talking about *true* science. However, there is real danger in-

---

[1] F. J. Moon and others, *Modern Biology* (Henry Holt, 1951), p. 634.

volved when one is talking about the *theory* of evolution, rather than about the *facts* of science.

When a person considers all the facts, he must accept either the position of a creationist or that of an evolutionist. Either he believes the Biblical account that man was created in the image of God, or he believes that man is just one of the higher animals and has developed from them. Evolution says, "The fossil record is good evidence that man himself did not appear suddenly on the earth in his present form, but has gradually developed from a much more primitive species."[2] The Bible says, "Then God said, Let us make man in our image, after our likeness" (Gen. 1:26). You must make your choice between the two.

The teaching which goes along with the theory of evolution says in connection with a belief in special creation, "We cannot really *know*."[3] The Bible says, "In the beginning God created the heaven and the earth." "Forever, O Lord, thy word is settled in heaven" (Ps. 119:89). You must make your choice between saying that the Word of God is true and forever settled, or saying that we cannot really know.

---

[2] Ella Thea Smith, *Exploring Biology*, p. 485.
[3] Gruenberg and Bingham, *Biology and Man*, p. 447.

Accepting the Genesis account of creation means that one must also accept the record of the fall of man and his need for redemption. The theory of evolution does not do this and so it cut out the very heart of the gospel message. It rules out the supernatural and substitutes materialistic evolution instead. There are even those in high religious circles who would seek to take away the very essentials of our Christian faith. Do not be misled into thinking that this shows a superior intellect. It merely shows that their eyes are blinded and their hearts are darkened. Around us we see the natural result—a neglect of God's Word and the failure to follow His teachings.

Creation and evolution are two mutually antagonistic ways of thinking. Creation is based on the unchanging, inspired Word of God, while evolution is based on speculation and assumption. It causes man to exalt himself and brings Christ down to the level of an ordinary human being.

One cannot accept both the Bible and evolution as truth. They are contradictory, not complementary or compatible.

This discussion has necessarily been brief, but the author hopes that two things have been made clear: first, that organic evolution is *not* a fact.

It is a theory which leads away from God and His Word. It is a teaching which should be recognized as being dangerous.

Second, that none of the so-called proofs of evolution will stand examination and in any way show themselves to be valid. The discontinuous record of the fossils of plants and animals as they are found in the rocks may be considered as one of the chief weaknesses of the evolutionary theory. In order to make the record seem more complete than it really is, large gaps have been filled in with reconstructions and guesses. These gaps are caused by plants and animals suddenly appearing with complex organs fully formed. The same thing is true of the appearance of man. There is no proof that he evolved from lower animals. He appears on the world scene with fully developed human physical and mental capacities.

Man was created to have fellowship with God. When Adam and Eve sinned, that fellowship was broken. "For just as all men die by virtue of their descent from Adam, so all such as are in union with Christ will be made alive again" (I Cor. 15: 22). It is His loving desire to restore you to a place of fellowship with Himself. Think of the privilege of being able to have communion with the One who created the universe! If this privilege is not already yours, may it soon become a reality in your life. Read these next few pages more carefully than any of the others. They may determine your eternal destiny. Evolution is not true, but there is no satisfaction in proving this alone. You want to know about your origin, but you should be even more vitally concerned about your final destination.

Chapter 18

LOOKING AHEAD

RIGHT now you may stand at a very puzzling place in your life and in history. Behind you have marched heroes of the faith who never heard of a chromosome, an Eohippus, or a Cro-Magnon man. Theirs was an unquestioning faith in the Bible as the very Word of God which no pseudo-science ever successfully attacked. They were reared in godly homes where from earliest childhood the Bible was read, believed, lived, and taught. They came to an early personal regenerating faith in Christ. No text or teacher drove a wedge of doubt into their trusting minds.

You stand today in the midst of a professing and powerless multitude. You want to know whether or not the Bible is the very Word of God. You have the right to know. Is it merely the sacred book of a few of the many millions of people of the world? Isn't sincerity of belief and a true endeavor in any religion all that is necessary in this life?

What right has one religious group to criticize or condemn another? Your heart and mind cry out to know the truth, while around you swirl the winds and storms of doubt, honest questioning, and scientific theories. What is the truth?

That was answered once for all when Christ said, "I am the way, the truth, and the life."

How can you know whether the Bible is the Word of God? It has stood the acid test of time. Other books have periods of popularity, but the Bible is always being printed and read by multitudes. It is the world's best seller year after year.

It is composed of many books or parts written by different human instruments. Long periods of time separate one portion from another. Yet there is a unity of theme and purpose that only a single mind could have maintained. Genesis is seen in Revelation. The law of Exodus is explained in Galatians. Leviticus blossoms in Hebrews, and Isaiah paints the portrait of the Christ who walks through the Gospels.

But you interrupt to say that each Gospel pictures a different Christ? No, they show Him in four aspects of His being. Matthew presents Him to the Jew as the Messiah fulfilling all spoken of Him by the prophets. Mark shows Him as a servant, obedient, prompt and busy. Luke would have us see the Son of Man. John pictures the everlasting Word of God become flesh; as Man, yet one with God the Father.

The Bible contains enough fulfilled prophecy to stagger the mind and cause the unbeliever truly to wonder. Caesar Augustus on his throne in Rome had no idea that he was fulfilling God's Word when he commanded that all go to their own cities to be taxed, at the very moment in time when Mary was to bring into the world the only-begotten Son of God. The scribes in Jerusalem knew the place of Christ's birth to tell to the Wise Men, for Micah had recorded it for the Lord hundreds of years before. The days in Egypt and the years in Nazareth all were promised before they happened. Titus laid Jerusalem and the Temple level with the ground in A.D. 70, as God's Word had decreed, and not a Christian was found within the walls. God had forewarned them through Luke to flee when they saw these things begin to come to pass.

The Jew is a sad and constant witness that the blood of Christ is indeed upon that nation and their children. He is still a byword among the nations and a stranger out of his native land until he returns to the Lord in belief.

The Bible contains power to impart life to a dead soul. "The entrance of thy words giveth light" (Ps. 119:30). "And that from childhood you have known the sacred Scriptures which can give you wisdom that leads to salvation through the faith that leans on Christ Jesus" (II Tim. 3:15). A single Bible verse with no human instrument can be used of God to lead a soul to salvation. No other book in the world can do this.

Where the Bible has gone, civilization and progress have followed. Hospitals, education, freedom, decency, law, and order are by-products of the Bible. Where it has been known and disregarded or distorted, abuses return, freedoms disappear and fear grips the heart of the multitudes.

Bible-reading and belief transform a life. After the soul is saved, the life is transfigured. Old things pass away as the Word takes its rightful place. Billy Sunday left his baseball for the privilege of preaching to hungry souls. Moody let someone else sell shoes while he won thousands to the Lord. Mary Slessor lived on in Africa after supplies were gone because she loved the black people and saw the gospel changing lives.

The person and work of Jesus Christ is the central theme of the Bible. What you think of Him and do with Him is the most important thing in your life. Time is but a speck between two eternities. Your life is a tiny part of time. When your few years have run their course, then what happens? Deep within the human heart lies a God-given knowledge that the soul lives on after the body dies. Immortality is woven into the very fabric of your being. Christ offers the only true answer to the future abode and condition of man after death.

Look now at Christ. Question yourself honestly. At this very time you may decide where you will spend eternity. Yes, you are the one who must decide. What do you think of Christ? Was He virgin-born? Was His life without blemish or spot? Was He God incarnate? Does His blood atone for sin? Did He die in your place? Did you, or will you, take Him as your Saviour? No sincerity of belief in a dead doctrine or a false religion can impart life. Life comes from life. Spiritual life comes from God through Christ. "I am the way, and the truth, and the life. No one can come to the Father, except through me" (John 14:6). There is one Way—Christ. There is one Door into eternity, blessed and joyful—Christ. How futile to grope blindly about a solid wall of untruth and doubt when there is an open door that surely leads to Heaven! How sad to try to climb up some other way where there is one way always open! How foolish to concoct theories and new religions when Truth beckons with nail-pierced hands!

Do you think the way is narrow? You want something real, vital, and of eternal value. You want a personal relationship with God. There is one way to accomplish your desire, through Christ. The way *is* narrow. It excludes all that is false. Truth is always narrow, else falsehood would enter and destroy. Bridges are narrow ways but they span engulfing floods. Sin would swallow us up and keep us from the true Way; but there is a bridge, Christ Himself. Doors look small when they are in huge walls, but they open into places of safety and rest. Come in through God's door, even Christ, and you will find rest and safety for your soul for time and eternity.

Look now to Him. By an act of simple faith you may be born into the family of God. Tell Him you believe His Son, Jesus Christ, died for your sin. As a young man and woman stand before the proper authorities and take each other as husband and wife, so you may stand before the God of Heaven and say, "I ...., take Thy Son to be my Saviour."

Yes, it is as simple as that, when you believe in your heart that He is who God says He is. Do this, and God will immediately give you power to become His child. He will impart to you His very life. You will experience regeneration, new birth, salvation, God-given life, in your inmost being. Then and then only will you know that no amount of sincerity can save. No heathen idol or civilized ritual can give satisfaction. No groping in darkness will lead to the light. No other belief can save. In the Bible alone is Christ revealed. Through Christ alone can God be found. No church, person, creed, or penance; no doing, giving, paying, or praying can avail outside of Christ. He alone is God's Lamb who takes away the sins of the world. There must be a personal acceptance of Him.

Search no longer for Truth. He stands outside the door of your heart. Open the door by faith and let Him in.

TEXTBOOKS	Pages Largely Devoted to Evolution	Similarity Proves Relationship	Proofs from Geology	Evolution of the Horse
Adventures with Animals and Plants E. Kroeber and W. H. Wolff D. C. Heath & Company, 1948	521-577	547-548	525-544	541-543
Basic Biology C. L. Fenton and P. E. Kambly Macmillan, 1947	500-544		501-533	529-531 534-535
Biology F. M. Wheat and E. T. Fitzpatrick American Book Co., 1949	407-475	456-457	412-440	432-436
Biology and Man B. C. Gruenberg and N. E. Bingham Ginn & Co., 1944	435-469 506-524	458	450-457	453
Biology for You B. B. Vance and D. F. Miller J. B. Lippincott Co., 1950	568-589	583	574-583	570
Biology in Daily Life F. D. Curtis and J. Urban Ginn & Co., 1949	465-475	51-53	465-469	468
Biology in Our Lives G. W. Hunter and F. K. Hunter American Book Co., 1949	369-378 408-419	412-413	372-378 408-410	408-409
Dynamic Biology Today A. O. Baker and L. H. Mills Rand McNally & Co., 1948	620-642	638-639	621 623-635	634-637
Everyday Biology F. C. Curtis, O. W. Caldwell, and Ginn & Co., 1946 Sherman	617-623	621	617-620	623
Exploring Biology Ella Thea Smith Harcourt, Brace, and Co., 1949	471-501		471-485	481-482
Modern Biology F. J. Moon and Others Henry Holt, 1951	426-429 652-665	655 659	653-655	655-657

Proofs from Classification	Proofs from Vestigial Structures	Proofs from Geographic Distribution	Proofs from Embryology			Prehistoric Man
			One-Celled Stage	Gill Slit Stage	Similarity of Embryos	
551	550	551-552		548	548-549	565-572
120-121		541-543				
487	457-458	453-456	460-461	461	461	441-449
37-39	460	460-463			459-460	515-516
578		571-572				584-588
51					460	
415	413	414-415		414	414	415-416
	631 639-640	631 635-638	640	640	640	
	621			621	574	
	486			485		483-485
74	658-659	661		659	659-660	426-429